Sarn

THE STORY OF AN OTTER

Story by Tessa Potter
Illustrations by Ken Lilly

Ⓐ

Andersen Press • London

*The author would like to thank Dr Gerald Legg
of the Booth Museum of Natural History, Brighton,
for his help and advice.*

Text copyright © 1996 by Tessa Potter. Illustrations copyright © 1996 by Ken Lilly.
The rights of Tessa Potter and Ken Lilly to be identified as the author and illustrator of this work have been
asserted by them in accordance with the Copyright, Designs and Patents Act, 1988.
First published in Great Britain in 1996 by Andersen Press Ltd., 20 Vauxhall Bridge Road, London SW1V
2SA. Published in Australia by Random House Australia Pty., 20 Alfred Street, Milsons Point, Sydney, NSW
2061. All rights reserved. Colour separated in Switzerland by Photolitho AG, Offsetreproduktionen, Gossau,
Zürich. Printed and bound in Italy by Grafiche AZ, Verona.

10   9   8   7   6   5   4   3   2   1

British Library Cataloguing in Publication Data available.
ISBN 0 86264 440 2

This book has been printed on acid-free paper

The young rabbits on Burrow Down were enjoying the spring sunshine. Nearby, a vixen hurried towards her earth. She needed shelter as she would soon give birth. She passed close by an old willow where, deep in the bank, an otter lay sleeping with her two cubs.

Evening came and the otter needed to find food. She left her cubs, who could not yet swim, and slipped silently into the river. She headed downstream to hunt for pike under the old bridge.

Sarn, the youngest of the cubs, was the first to wake. He was hungry. He dashed out of the holt, mewing and calling for his mother. The second cub joined him and, forgetting their hunger, they scrambled up the bank and began to play.

At last, they heard their mother's low whistle. She climbed the bank, holding a fish tightly between her teeth. Sarn sniffed and pawed at the fish and his mother tore off small pieces for the cubs. Sarn gulped them down, whining for more and pulling at his mother's muzzle.

Gently shaking off the cubs, the mother otter
ran off towards the Great Wood.
She called to the cubs to follow closely.
She was taking them to catch eels
in Willow Pool. The cubs bounded after
her, trying hard to keep up. As they
passed, they frightened a mole who fled
to the safety of her tunnels.

They came to a shallow stream. The eldest cub splashed after his mother, but Sarn stood whimpering at the edge. His mother ran on, thinking he would follow.

Suddenly, Sarn stopped whining. A dark,
terrible shadow was coming
towards him, gliding through the trees,
swooping down over the water.
Sarn cowered low on the ground, terrified.

His mother turned and saw the owl
hovering over her little cub.
She let out a furious cry. The owl soared away.
Sarn's mother ran to him and dragged
him across the stream. Now
Sarn knew why he must stay close.

At last the three otters came to the pool. The mother slipped into the water, leaving the cubs by the reeds. Sarn stared anxiously after her, frightened now of being left behind.

Then something caught his eye on the bank. He saw a frog making its way to the pool. Sarn gave a little, excited growl and tried to grab it with his paws. He missed and the frog hopped into the reeds. Sarn desperately wanted the frog, but each time he pounced, the frog hopped further away. He splashed after it, further and further into the shallows.

Suddenly, Sarn's feet were no longer touching the bottom. He fell right under the water. Down and down he sank. He tried to yelp in fright and water rushed into his mouth. Then he bobbed up to the surface, spluttering and choking.

Frantically, Sarn paddled his paws
up and down. He found he stayed
afloat, and soon he was moving
through the water, no longer afraid.

Sarn's mother swam over to
him, nudging and stroking him
with her nose. She was proud of
her cub. He hadn't managed to
catch a frog, but little Sarn had
learnt to swim.

Look back at the story. Can you find...

A **burying beetle** burying a dead shrew.

An **earwig** standing guard over her eggs.

A male **mallard** swimming on the river. The female is hidden on her nest in the tree.

A **centipede** catching an earwig with its poisonous claws.

A **brimstone butterfly**.

A **millipede** eating a leaf. If it is attacked, the millipede will curl up and give off a foul-smelling liquid.

A **great diving beetle** catching a mayfly nymph.

A **nuthatch** making her nest in an old woodpecker's hole.

A **mute swan** sitting on her nest.

A **marsh marigold**.

A **woodlouse**. It keeps its eggs in pockets under its body until the tiny babies hatch.

A **banded snail**.

A **badger** out looking for food.

A **queen bumble bee** looking for a hole to lay her eggs in.

A **dandelion**.

A **kingfisher** watching for fish.

A **tawny owl** hunting.

White willow catkins. **Alder catkins.**

A **fox**.

A **caddisfly larva** in its case of tiny stones and sticks.

A **dragonfly nymph** catching a watershrimp.

A **common dog violet**.

A **mayfly nymph** being caught by a diving beetle.

A **hunting spider** catching a woodlouse.

A **roe deer** hiding in the trees.

THINGS TO DO

MAKE A MINI WILDLIFE HABITAT.

You will need earth, old leaves, broken flowerpots,
stones, old bricks, bits of wood or logs.

Make your mini habitat in a shady corner of garden or backyard.
Before long you will find many different kinds of small creatures living there.
Lift up the logs and stones carefully - put them back in the same place.

On the previous page you will find pictures of some of the creatures you may find, like millipedes, earwigs and centipedes. You are sure to find snails and slugs and their eggs. You may see many kinds of spiders and their webs and egg sacs. Look up the names of the different beetles you see.